Tanya Gets a Gift

Written by Isabel Thomas

Illustrated by Alex Naidoo

Tanya gets a gift from Gran.

They go to the shops.

You can spend it in this shop.

Tanya grabs a red rocket.

Then she sees a boat.

A boat might be fun.

Then she sees a ping-pong set.

I need this.
I will get this ping-pong set!

7

Then she sees the books.
They all look good.

At last, Tanya sees just the thing.

Gran, I will get that!

Talk about the story

Ask your child these questions:

1 Where did Tanya and Gran go?

2 What things did Tanya look at?

3 What did Tanya buy in the end?

4 How did Gran feel about the gift?

5 What would you have bought in the shop?

6 Do you prefer to get a gift or give a gift?

Can your child retell the story using their own words?